D0513665

THE SECOND LITTLE
BOOK OF
Fred

Since Rupert Fawcett invented Fred ten years ago
Fred has become something of a star with books
and merchandise in several countries.

Fred's past life is documented in Rupert's nine
previous books: *Fred, More Fred, The Extraordinary
World of Fred, The Continued Adventures of Fred,
Carry on Fred, At Home with Fred, Pure Fred,
The One and Only Fred* and *The Little Book of Fred.*
Fred can also be seen in the *Mail on Sunday.*

The Second Little Book of Fred contains sixty-one
new Fred illustrations depicting Fred's strange life
with the good-natured Penelope and ever-present
black cat, Anthony.

Copyright © 1999 Rupert Fawcett

The right of Rupert Fawcett to be identified as the Author
of the Work has been asserted by him in accordance with the
Copyright, Designs and Patents Act 1988.

First published in 1999
by HEADLINE BOOK PUBLISHING

10 9 8 7 6 5 4 3 2 1

All rights reserved. No part of this publication may be
reproduced, stored in a retrieval system, or transmitted,
in any form or by any means without the prior written
permission of the publisher, nor be otherwise circulated
in any form of binding or cover other than that in which
it is published and without a similar condition being
imposed on the subsequent purchaser.

ISBN 0 7472 7421 5

Printed and bound in Italy by
Canale & C. S.p.A

HEADLINE BOOK PUBLISHING
A division of the Hodder Headline Group
338 Euston Road
London NW1 3BH

www.headline.co.uk
www.hodderheadline.com

THE SECOND LITTLE BOOK OF

Fred

Rupert Fawcett

HEADLINE

FRED'S FIRST ATTEMPT AT FILM-MAKING WAS A FLY-ON-THE-WALL DOCUMENTARY

ALTHOUGH PENELOPE HAD NO OBJECTION
TO GETTING OLDER SHE WAS NOT
HAPPY ABOUT THE CROW'S FEET

FRED HAD OFTEN WONDERED WHAT
PENELOPE GOT UP TO IN THE CELLAR

FRED WAS ONLY PREPARED TO
TAKE HIS MOTHER-IN-LAW ON
HOLIDAY ON CERTAIN CONDITIONS

PENELOPE HAD ALWAYS SUSPECTED
THAT FRED HAD ANOTHER LIFE

FRED AND PENELOPE'S MORNING
ABLUTIONS WERE CHOREOGRAPHED
TO PERFECTION

UNFORTUNATELY FOR FRED THERE HAD
BEEN A BIT OF A MIX-UP DOWN
AT THE STRIPPAGRAM AGENCY

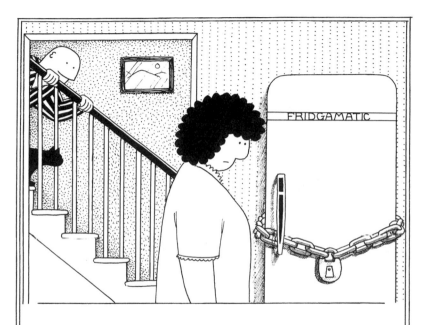

PENELOPE SENSED THAT FRED
WAS ON TO HER

FRED AND PENELOPE WERE GREAT
BELIEVERS IN FORWARD PLANNING

FRED NEVER WENT ANYWHERE
WITHOUT HIS MOBILE

WHEN FRED ORGANISED A REUNION OF
HIS OLD PRIMARY SCHOOL PALS HE
WAS DELIGHTED TO DISCOVER
THAT THEY HADN'T CHANGED A BIT

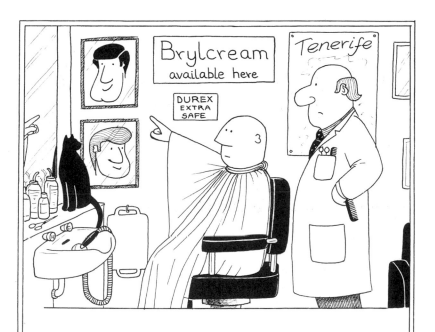

FRED'S BARBER HAD ALWAYS
REGARDED HIM AS A TIME-WASTER

PENELOPE WONDERED IF THERE REALLY
WOULD BE A MARKET FOR FRED'S
LATEST INVENTION, THE
HANDS-FREE BREAD KNIFE.

IN FRED'S CASE ONE PSYCHOTHERAPIST
WAS NOT ENOUGH

AFTER A COUPLE OF GLASSES OF
WINE FRED COULD SENSE PENELOPE
BEGINNING TO UNWIND

FRED HAD VARIOUS METHODS FOR
GETTING RID OF UNWANTED GUESTS

AFTER WEEKS OF RESEARCH FRED
FINALLY TRACED THE HOME ADDRESS
OF HIS OLD SCHOOL BULLY

FRED WAS DISAPPOINTED THAT
PENELOPE HAD DECIDED TO
KISS AND TELL

FRED SENSED THAT PENELOPE WAS
UNHAPPY WITH HER NEW HAIRCUT

'MY VERY OWN MILLENNIUM DOME',
SIGHED FRED

FRED AND PENELOPE
MADE A GREAT TEAM

PENELOPE WAS ALREADY
BEGINNING TO REGRET HER
NEW YEARS RESOLUTION

FRED AND PENELOPE COULDN'T WAIT
TO INVITE THEIR FRIENDS ROUND
TO SHOW OFF THEIR NEW LUXURY
DEEP-PILE CARPET

FRED WAS KEEN TO DISCUSS THE
CHRISTMAS CREDIT CARD STATEMENT
WITH PENELOPE

FROM THE MOMENT HE WAS
BORN FRED SEEMED SOMEHOW
DIFFERENT FROM OTHER BABIES

PENELOPE'S MODEL OF THE BANK
MANAGER WAS A REMARKABLY
GOOD LIKENESS

FRED WAS DETERMINED TO MAKE
AN IMPRESSION ON THE NEW
NEXT-DOOR NEIGHBOURS

FRED SENSED THAT PENELOPE
HAD ALREADY OPENED THE
CHRISTMAS SHERRY

PENELOPE COULDN'T HELP FEELING THAT
FRED'S ATTEMPT AT LANDSCAPE
GARDENING LACKED IMAGINATION

FRED FELT HIS CHRISTMAS GUESTS
HAD OVERSTAYED THEIR WELCOME

WITH THE ASSISTANCE OF A FEW
FRIENDS FRED FINALLY UNVEILED HIS
LATEST LABOUR-SAVING CREATION,
THE SIX-HEADED HAMMER

MONDAY STARTED BADLY

FRED MODIFIED HIS LAWNMOWER
SO THAT EVERY TIME HE USED
IT HE AUTOMATICALLY GOT
A PAT ON THE BACK

FRED AND PENELOPE WERE
DELIGHTED TO DISCOVER THAT
THE NEW NEXT-DOOR NEIGHBOURS
WERE THEIR KIND OF PEOPLE

FORTUNATELY FRED AND PENELOPE'S
ARGUMENT OVER WHO SHOULD HAVE
THE LAST CHOCOLATE HOBNOB
ENDED IN PEACE TALKS

FRED ALWAYS MADE A BIT OF A DRAMA
OUT OF CARVING THE SUNDAY JOINT

DURING TESTING OF HIS LATEST
INVENTION, THE 'WINTER DOGGY
SUIT' FRED REALISED IT HAD
ONE GLARING DESIGN FAULT

FRED AND PENELOPE'S MARRIAGE WAS
GOING THROUGH ONE OF ITS
DIFFICULT PHASES

'AS SOON AS HE GETS BEHIND
THE WHEEL OF A CAR HE TURNS
INTO A COMPLETE ANIMAL',
SIGHED PENELOPE

FRED AND PENELOPE DIDNT OFTEN
FIGHT BUT WHEN THEY DID IT WAS
USUALLY OVER THE LITTLE
THINGS IN LIFE

FRED LIKED TO THINK OF HIMSELF
AS AN ENTREPRENEUR

EVERYONE THOUGHT THE TURKEY
LOOKED A LITTLE UNDERDONE

BY THE SECOND BOTTLE OF WINE
FRED AND PENELOPE'S MILLENNIUM
CELEBRATION WAS STARTING
TO GO WITH A SWING

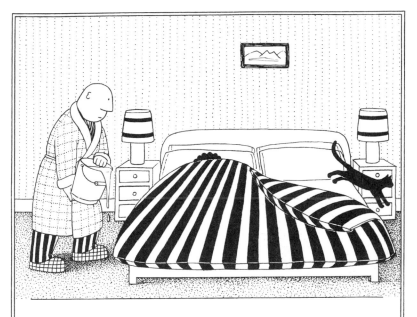

PENELOPE OFTEN REQUIRED A
LITTLE EXTRA HELP WITH GETTING
UP IN THE MORNING

FOR THEIR THIRD COURSE FRED
OPTED FOR THE CHEESEBOARD
WHILE PENELOPE HAD THE
SWEET TROLLEY

PENELOPE WAS PLEASED TO SEE
FRED AND HER MOTHER
GETTING ON FOR A CHANGE

WHILE PENELOPE WARMED THE POT
FRED POPPED UPSTAIRS FOR ONE OF
HIS EXTRA-STRONG TEA BAGS

THEY DIDN'T CALL FRED 'SILENT-
BUT-DEADLY-FRED' FOR NOTHING

IT ALWAYS MADE PENELOPE SAD
TO SEE FRED MIGRATE

HIGH ON EVERY TOURIST'S ITINERARY
WAS A TRIP TO FRED'S HOUSE TO SEE
'THE CHANGING OF THE SHEETS'

FRED HAD BEEN LOOKING FORWARD TO
HIS BIRTHDAY PARTY FOR MONTHS

OVER THE YEARS FRED GOT
USED TO PENELOPE'S
VERBAL DIARRHOEA

PENELOPE INSISTED ON
EXTREMELY SAFE SEX

VALENTINE'S DAY COULD MEAN ONLY
ONE THING – A ROMANTIC WINDOW
TABLE FOR TWO AT FRED'S
FAVOURITE RESTAURANT

AFTER MONTHS OF WAITING, FRED
AND PENELOPE FINALLY RECEIVED
PLANNING PERMISSION FOR THEIR
NASAL EXTENSIONS

PENELOPE SO ENJOYED BACK-SEAT
DRIVING THAT SHE DECIDED TO HAVE
THE CAR SPECIALLY MODIFIED

FRED FOUND THE PERFECT PLACE
TO BE FOR THE MILLENNIUM
CELEBRATIONS

ON THE OCCASION OF HER BIRTHDAY
FRED INSISTED ON GIVING PENELOPE
BREAKFAST IN BED

PENELOPE WAS FULL OF ADMIRATION
FOR FRED'S DEDICATION TO THE
NEIGHBOURHOOD WATCH SCHEME

PEOPLE COULDN'T HELP BUT BE
IMPRESSED BY FRED'S PIGEONS